The World's Most Challenging Puzzles

Charles Barry Townsend

Sterling Publishing Co., Inc.   New York

DEDICATION

This book is dedicated to that matchless group of friends that have lent color and substance to our lives: Dick and Carol, Frank and Jane, Arthur and Sandy, Mickey and Ronnie, Stan and Gloria, Whit and Bobbie.

Edited by Timothy Nolan

Library of Congress Cataloging-in-Publication Data

Townsend, Charles Barry.
  The world's most challenging puzzles / by Charles Barry Townsend.
     p.   cm.
  Includes index.
  ISBN 0-8069-6730-7
  1. Puzzles.   I. Title
BV1493.T687 1988
793.73—dc19   88-19729
                                                                   CIP

        1   3   5   7   9   10   8   6   4   2

Copyright © 1988 by Charles Barry Townsend
Published by Sterling Publishing Co., Inc.
Two Park Avenue, New York, N.Y. 10016
Distributed in Canada by Oak Tree Press Ltd.
% Canadian Manda Group, P.O. Box 920, Station U
Toronto, Ontario, Canada M8Z 5P9
Distributed in Great Britain and Europe by Cassell PLC
Artillery House, Artillery Row, London SW1P 1RT, England
Distributed in Australia by Capricorn Ltd.
P.O. Box 665, Lane Cove, NSW 2066
Manufactured in the United States of America
All rights reserved
Sterling ISBN 0-8069-6730-7 Trade

Contents

Introduction

Once again I have the privilege of presenting, for your entertainment, a mixed bag of some of the finest puzzles and problems that have appeared over the past 100 years. To emphasize the roots and longevity of some of the posers, I would like to mention that several of the best are from the pen of that famous Victorian writer Angelo Lewis, better known as Professor Hoffmann. During his long and productive life, Professor Hoffmann wrote many books and magazine articles dealing with that triad of mental entertainment: puzzles, games and magic. His great book of problems, *Puzzles Old and New*, which first appeared in 1893, is crammed with hundreds of puzzles that are still found in many current books dealing with these pastimes.

Besides the Professor's contributions, you will find a variety of material that will really tax your powers of bring-

The author, with sons Chris and Mark, and the World's Most Challenging Cardhouse.

ing order out of chaos, dealing with bread, golden ropes, coins, eggs, magnets, bottles, a milk train, a "frat" puzzle from Sam Loyd, a buzzsaw, a spider web, and many, many more. In fact, you'll be challenged 95 times before reaching the end. So, turn off the television, sit back in your chair, put on your thinking cap and let the games begin!

Charles Barry Townsend

Remember, when you've had enough, answers start on page 101.

PUZZLES

The Most Challenging "Geometry" Puzzle

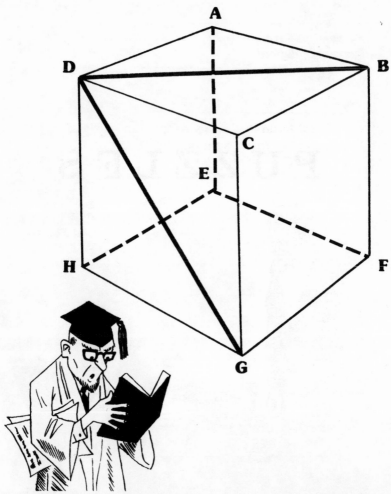

The professor is in a quandary. He's forgotten the answer to the puzzle pictured above and class begins in five minutes! Two lines, *BD* and *GD*, are drawn on the faces of an imaginary cube. Both lines converge at point *D*. Can you calculate the angle between these two diagonal lines and help the professor out?

The Most Challenging "Coffee" Puzzle

"But, Sir, I assure you that that is a fresh cup of coffee!"

"Balderdash, young man! This is the same cup of coffee that I sent back. Get the manager at once!"

Our waiter is in trouble now. Mr. Fussbudget found a fly in his after-dinner coffee and sent it back. When his fresh cup arrived he took one sip and knew the waiter had given him back the same cup without the fly. How did Mr. Fussbudget know that the waiter was trying to flimflam him?

The Most Challenging "Tombstone" Puzzle

Sacred to the memory of
MR. EDWARD FOUNTAIN
of this parish, who died
on the 28th Oct. 1823:
AGED 66 YEARS
also of
MRS. SARAH FOUNTAIN
his widow, who died
on the 23rd Sept. 1812
AGED 82 YEARS

The Reverend I. N. Spire chanced upon the above tombstone while on his way to vespers. Something about the inscription bothered him. After a moment's reflection he discovered an error in it. Can you find the Reverend's revelation?

The Most Challenging "Magic Square" Puzzle

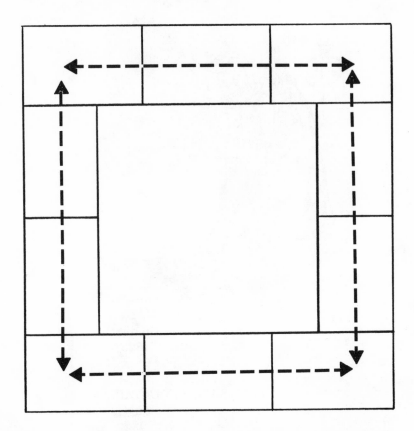

Now, here's a novel way to construct a magic square. From a deck of playing cards remove ten cards, ace through ten, and, counting the ace as one, arrange them in a square in such a way that the sum of the cards on any side is eighteen. If you set them down as shown above, the three cards in the top and bottom rows must add up to eighteen and the four cards in each of the side columns must also add up to eighteen.

The Most Challenging "Tennis Ball" Puzzle

Harriet has discovered a gopher hole on the courts of the Idle Hours Country Club. The hole where her tennis ball now resides is too deep to reach into and the bend in its middle makes retrieving the ball with a stick out of the question. Undaunted, Harriet quickly figures out the best way to free the ball and has it back in service within two minutes. How can she do this without digging up the court?

The Most Challenging "Thimble" Puzzle

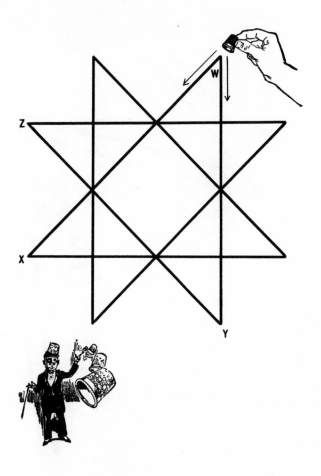

Thomas Thackery, the King of Thaumaturgical Thimble Trickery, presents this problem: Put seven thimbles on seven points of the above star by placing a thimble on an empty point of the star and then sliding it over to another empty point. On the move pictured here, the thimble could end up either at point *X* or point *Y*. Don't get stuck by this puzzle.

The Most Challenging "Chalk" Puzzle

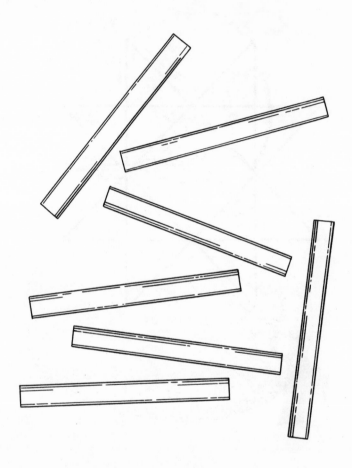

Get set to chalk this puzzle up to experience. All you have to do is take seven new pieces of chalk and lay them out so that every piece touches every other piece. If you can squeak through this problem in under thirty minutes, you're a genius.

The Most Challenging "Bakery" Puzzle

This is a puzzle with a twist. Olaf has just removed a piping-hot loaf of his famous "Poppy Seed Pretzel Puzzle Bread" from the oven. As his customers draw near, he asks them, "If I take my knife and make one straight cut across any part of the loaf, what is the maximum number of pieces I can divide it into?" Can you taste the answer to this delectable problem?

The Most Challenging "Goblet" Puzzle

Here's an interesting after-dinner puzzle. Borrow a coin from someone and bet him that you can balance the coin on the rim of an empty glass in such a way that more than two-thirds of the coin will be hanging over the edge. You are allowed to use the forks, but the two forks can touch the coin but cannot touch either the glass or the table. This problem should keep you in spare change.

The Most Challenging "Bicycle" Puzzle

At the turn of the century, Atlantic City was famed for its miles and miles of boardwalk. Every summer, Waylan Armstrong was out on the boards perambulating Mother Armstrong down to the Steel Pier and back. Waylan was very consistent in his rate of speed: Against a stiff wind he could pedal a mile in four minutes, but with the same wind at his back he could pedal a mile in three minutes. Given these facts, can you figure out how long it took him to ride a mile on a calm day? If you solve this in less than five minutes you deserve a box of Salt Water Taffy.

The Most Challenging "Match" Puzzle

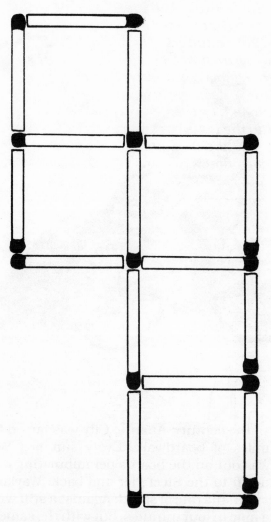

Lay out sixteen matches as pictured, so that they form five squares all the same size. Now, reposition two of the matches so that there are only four squares the same size. It sounds easy, but. . . .

The Most Challenging "Coin" Puzzle

"All right, Dear, listen carefully. On the table are three coins: two quarters and a nickel. The nickel is between the quarters. The problem is to place one of the quarters in the middle instead of the nickel. When moving the coins you must adhere to the following rules: The first quarter can be moved but not touched; the nickel can be touched but not moved, and the last quarter can either be touched or moved. This is the quarter that we want to place between the other two coins. Think that you can solve the puzzle?"

"Farlow, hit the road. It's three in the morning."

The Most Challenging "Egg" Puzzle

Albert, that prince of butlers, was honored by the Puzzle Club the other night. Albert submitted the following winning gastronomic quiz: "How would you go about boiling a two-minute egg if you only had two sand timers—one for five minutes and the other for three minutes—to time it with?" Albert received a standing ovation for this one. Can you crack this problem before the sand runs out?

The Most Challenging "Magnet" Puzzle

The monthly Puzzle Club meeting is about to start. To be admitted, you have to answer a question propounded by the Sergeant at Arms: "You are given two identical iron bars. One is a magnet, the other an ordinary piece of iron. You are to identify which of the bars is the magnet by placing them together in a certain way. You can only do this once and nothing else may be used in your determination." How will you go about solving this problem?

The Most Challenging "Glass" Puzzle

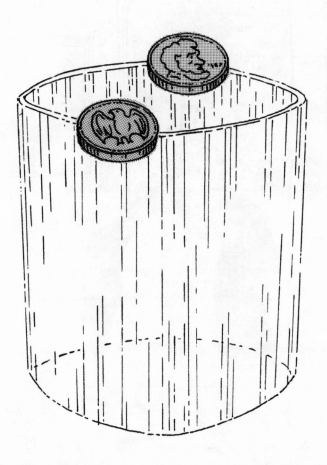

Here's an experiment in dexterity and a good bet at the dinner table. Take two quarters and balance them on the rim of a water glass as shown. Now challenge anyone to pick off both coins from the glass at the same moment, using only two fingers of one hand. The solution to this puzzle is a snap.

The Most Challenging "Card" Puzzle

"*I give up! This blasted puzzle can't be solved!*"

Our hero seems to be at the end of his rope. Let's help him out. The puzzle states that you must take the four fives from a deck of cards and lay them out on the table face up in such a way that only sixteen of the twenty *large* pips on the cards show. You have ten minutes to solve this one.

The Most Challenging "Rope" Puzzle

Our levitating swami has his own version of the "Indian Rope Trick" for you to solve. On his platform is a plain piece of rope. Pick up the ends of the rope, one in each hand, and tie a knot in the middle. The catch is that you are not allowed to let go of either end of the rope while doing this. Don't get up in the air trying to work this one out.

The Most Challenging "Soda Bottle" Puzzle

This is one of those "betcha" puzzles. After you finish drinking a bottle of soda, put it down on the table, reach into your pocket and remove a half-dollar and tell your friends that you can put a half-dollar into a bottle without damaging the bottle in any way. As impossible as this feat seems, you will be able to accomplish it with ease.

The Most Challenging "Area" Puzzle

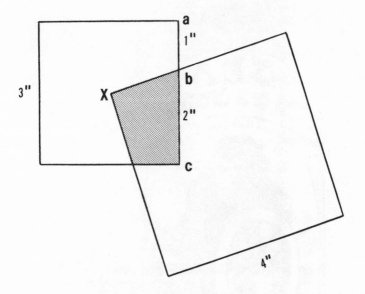

This is a neat little geometry problem. Pictured here are two squares, one three inches on a side, the other four inches on a side. The upper left corner of the four-inch square is anchored to the middle of the smaller square at point X. The larger square has been rotated until its upper side crosses line *ac* at point *b*. Using the information given in the illustration, can you quickly calculate the area, in square inches, of the shaded portion of the drawing?

The Most Challenging "Milk Train" Puzzle

Back in 1870, with the opening of the first regular transcontinental railway service, an enterprising young man decided that he could make money shipping milk from New York to California by train. To make it pay, he would have to find a way to ship it without freezing it or refrigerating it. He also couldn't afford cans, bottles, or containers of any kind. Finally, after working on the problem for weeks he came up with a solution. How did he do it?

The Most Challenging "Lunch" Puzzle

"I'll take that bet—and if I lose I'll buy dinner, too!"

The Boss

When the boss's lunch arrived, a $6.00 triple-decker sandwich from the Stage Door Deli, Treadmill walked over and placed an empty wastebasket over it and said, "Chief, I'll bet you 50¢ that I can eat your sandwich without touching the wastebasket, the table or the plate it's on. In fact, I won't touch anything in the room nor will anyone else help me out in any way. Do we have a wager?"

How did Treadmill win his bet?

The Most Challenging "Scissors" Puzzle

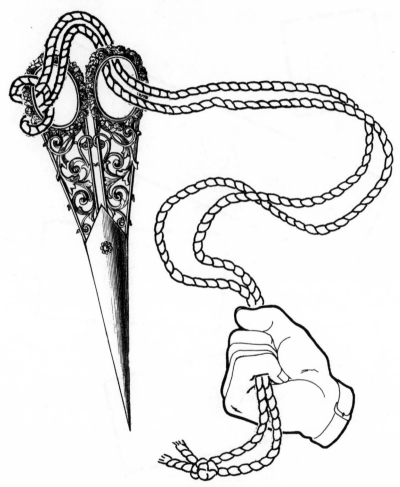

The following puzzle is driving them up the wall down at the Yarn Barn. Take a stout piece of cord and thread it through the bows of a pair of scissors (as shown); then knot the ends together. Now, challenge anyone to release the scissors without cutting the cord while you maintain a firm grip on the ends of the cord. It's easier (or harder) than you think.

The Most Challenging "Rectangle" Puzzle

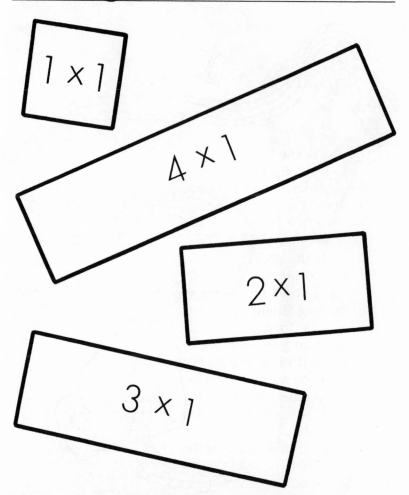

Here's a great "gotcha" problem. Place these four rectangular pieces of cardboard on a table and invite a friend to arrange them so that they form a perfect square. The numbers indicate the size of the pieces in inches. Suffice it to say that after all fail you will show them the way. Of course, you have to try it yourself before turning to the solution.

The Most Challenging "Cord" Puzzle

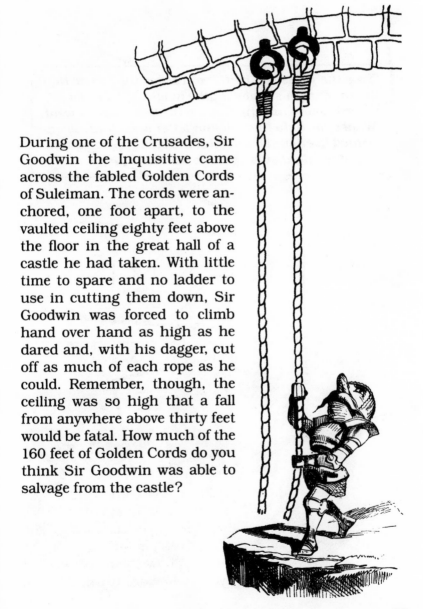

During one of the Crusades, Sir Goodwin the Inquisitive came across the fabled Golden Cords of Suleiman. The cords were anchored, one foot apart, to the vaulted ceiling eighty feet above the floor in the great hall of a castle he had taken. With little time to spare and no ladder to use in cutting them down, Sir Goodwin was forced to climb hand over hand as high as he dared and, with his dagger, cut off as much of each rope as he could. Remember, though, the ceiling was so high that a fall from anywhere above thirty feet would be fatal. How much of the 160 feet of Golden Cords do you think Sir Goodwin was able to salvage from the castle?

The Most Challenging "Four-Letter Word" Puzzle

"Stop the presses, Chief! I've cracked the puzzle that the Dutchman shouted at the judge after he sentenced him to twenty years in the big house. It went, 'What's the only English four-letter word that, when printed in capitals, will read the same upside down as it does right side up?' The word is. . . ."

The Most Challenging "Number" Puzzle

77, 49, 36, 18...? What number is next above?

Mr. Howard Distin, a maker of musical instruments long ago, was trying to "drum up" some business with a numbers contest. During the annual instrument convention he printed the above progression puzzle on a drumhead hoping to snare some interest in his display. Do you know what the next number should be in this series?

The Most Challenging "Star" Puzzle

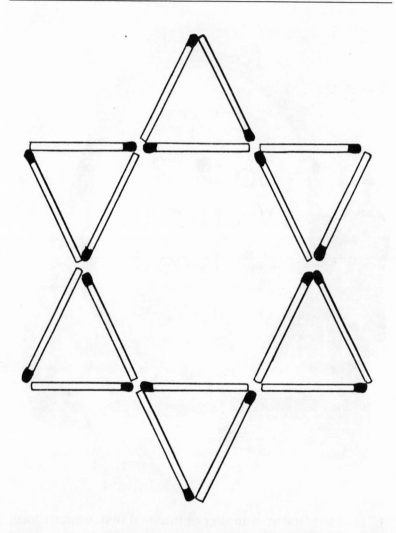

You're apt to get starry-eyed trying to work this one out. The above eighteen matches form a star comprised of eight big and little triangles. What you have to do is remove just two of the matches so that you have only six triangles. It's your turn now.

The Most Challenging "Frat" Puzzle

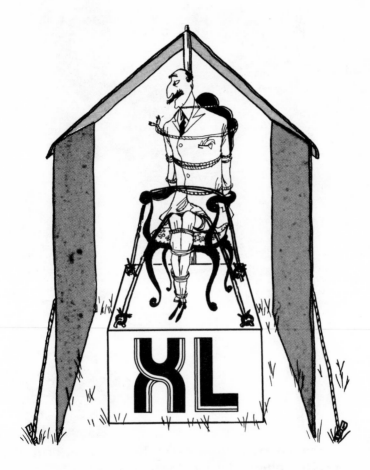

During hazing week at a local university, the fraternity brothers tied up one of the freshmen and put him in a tent. Can you answer the following questions about him?

- How do you know that he is not a young man?
- How do you know that he is a scholar?
- How do you know that he is smarter than his fellow students?

The Most Challenging "Salt and Pepper" Puzzle

It seems that Gwendolyn has seen her boss perform this trick once too often. Herbert loves to amaze his friends with this puzzle. After pouring a small mound of salt on the table he then sprinkles it with a liberal amount of pepper. The puzzle, he tells his guests, is to remove the pepper from the salt without touching either the salt or the pepper. Although this sounds impossible, clever Herbert can do it in one minute flat. Can you discover the secret and make Gwendolyn yawn, too?

The Most Challenging "Pencil" Puzzle

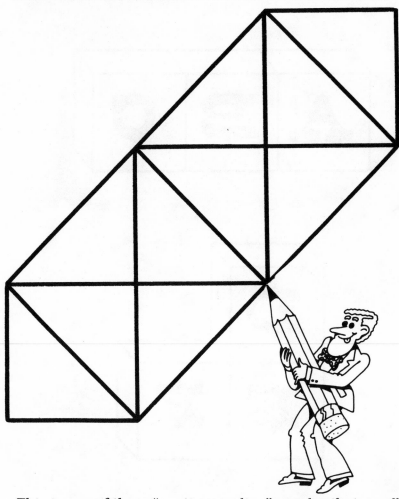

This is one of those "continuous line" puzzles that we all love so much. Take pencil in hand and duplicate the figure shown above. To accomplish this you have to use one continuous line; the line cannot cross itself at any point, cannot go over any part of the line more than once, and must end at the point indicated by the tip of the pencil in the hands of the young artist pictured here.

The Most Challenging "Block" Puzzle

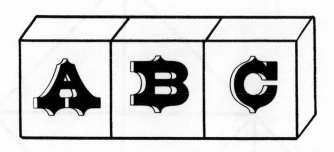

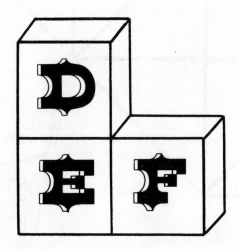

We're going back to school for this puzzle—way, way back.
If you take three wooden cubes, or blocks, and glue them
squarely face to face, only two different configurations are
possible (as illustrated), but how many different shapes
can you construct with four cubes? Please don't get stuck
on your first try!

The Most Challenging "Theatre" Puzzle

Back in 1905 that famous theatre of magic, the Sphinx, opened to an enthusiastic audience. The theatre had one hundred seats and on that first day they sold every one of them and took in exactly $100. The admissions were as follows: men, $5.00 each; women, $2.00 each; and children, 10¢ each. Using this information, can you calculate how many men, women and children took in this premiere performance?

The Most Challenging "Age" Puzzle

He: Now let's see if I have this puzzle right—how many children does your sister have?

She: Joan has three children.

He: And how old are they?

She: The product of their ages is 36.

He: I need to know more than that!

She: The sum of their ages is the same as my street address, and you know what number I live at.

He: I still need more information!

She: The oldest one likes tennis.

He: Okay, now I know their ages!

Whether it's a foxtrot or a foxy problem, Fred is fast on his feet. Is there enough information here for you to determine the ages of Joan's three children?

The Most Challenging "Sting" Puzzle

Be prepared to get stung on this one. On the table are nine coins totalling 80¢. As you can see, there is 20¢ in heads showing and 60¢ in tails showing. The puzzle is to turn over 25¢ worth of coins and leave 40¢ in heads showing. I think that I'll be "buzzing" along before you read the answer to this one!

The Most Challenging "Vase" Puzzle

Mr. Peckinpaw, an avid collector of oriental vases, is about to have a shattering experience. You can help him put things back together. First, trace the outline of the vase onto another sheet of paper and cut it out. Then, cut this outline into three pieces with two straight cuts. Finally, take these three pieces and rearrange them to form a perfect square. Make a special note of Mr. Peckinpaw's vase's symmetry.

The Most Challenging "Fish" Puzzle

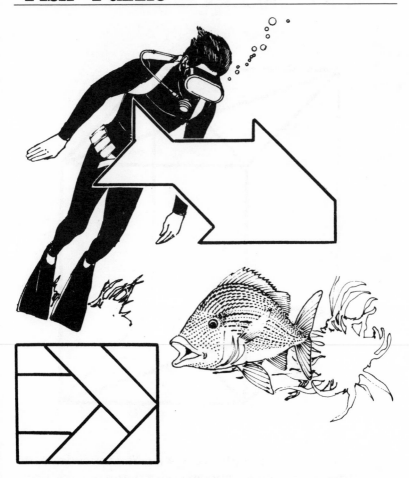

Certainly one of the most enduring forms of mechanical puzzles in the world is the tangram. It has been around for hundreds of years.

Pictured is an oblong set of tangram tiles. Above it is the outline of an oriental fighting fish. The puzzle, of course, is to rearrange the seven tangram tiles into the shape of this fish. Can you picture how this is done? Don't get hooked now; it's not as easy as it looks.

The Most Challenging "3-D" Puzzle

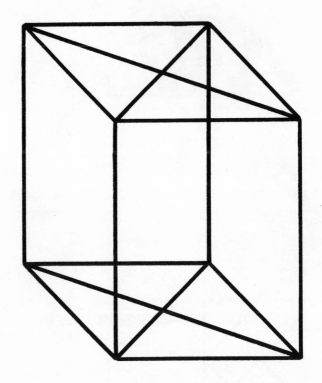

Here is another puzzle with a real twist. You must draw the three-dimensional figure shown above using one continuous line. At no point can the line cross itself. However, you must keep in mind that this is a *three-dimensional figure* and some of the lines go *behind* and *under* as well as *over* and *in front of* other lines. In other words, although you draw this figure on a two-dimensional surface, you must pretend that you are drawing it in space. When one line crosses another line, it may really be going behind it or in front of it.

The Most Challenging "Buzz Saw" Puzzle

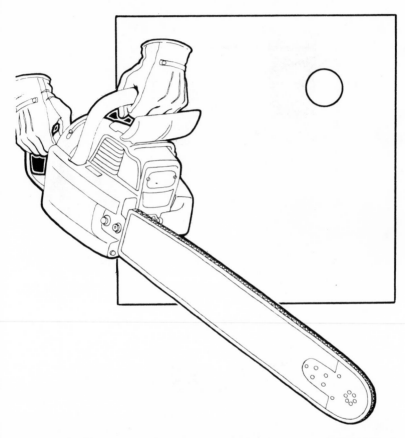

Buzz Saw Bailey dropped into the Grits-n-Bits coffee shop the other day and told everyone about a puzzle he had just heard about from a lumber salesman. The salesman showed Bailey a square piece of wood with a small hole drilled in it off-center. "The problem," he told Bailey, "is to figure out the least number of pieces the board would have to be cut up into so that when you reassembled the pieces the hole would then be in the center of the board." Can you figure out the answer?

The Most Challenging "Light" Puzzle

STOVE

OIL LAMP

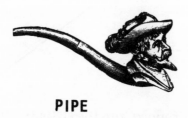

PIPE

Many years ago Boondock Bentley was out hunting. After walking through the snow all day he arrived, cold and exhausted, at his cabin deep in the forest as night was falling. In his cabin he had a pipe, an oil lamp and a wood-burning stove. Unfortunately, he only had one match. Which item should Bentley light first?

The Most Challenging "Word" Puzzle

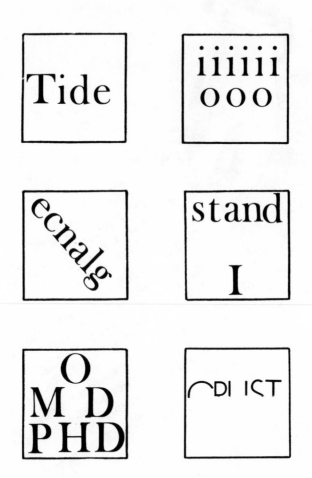

These six "word pictures" all stand for some object or expression. Four out of six is a passing grade on this one.

The Most Challenging "Perception" Puzzle

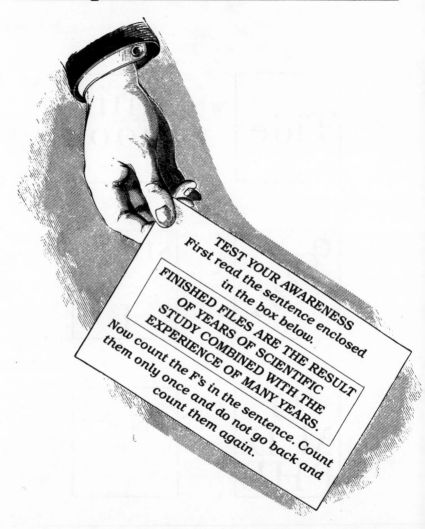

TEST YOUR AWARENESS
First read the sentence enclosed
in the box below.

FINISHED FILES ARE THE RESULT
OF YEARS OF SCIENTIFIC
STUDY COMBINED WITH THE
EXPERIENCE OF MANY YEARS.

Now count the F's in the sentence. Count
them only once and do not go back and
count them again.

The above puzzle is printed on the back of a business card used by the G & C Auto Body Shop of Passaic, New Jersey. It's an interesting test in perception, a skill that their clients sometimes lack. Let's see how you score on this test.

The Most Challenging "Country" Puzzle

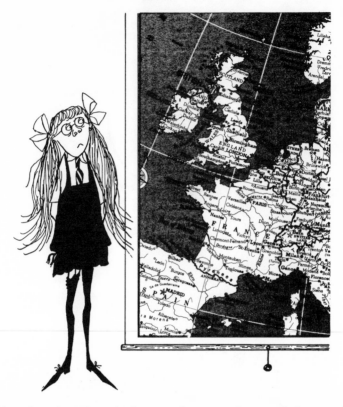

"All right, Cynthia, let's see what you learned this year in school. From the five following hints you should be able to deduce the name of the country we're looking for. The numbers refer to positional letters within the country's name and are used to form words."

- My 1, 2, 7 is an extreme point.
- My 3, 4, 5, 7 is what the reader will be when he solves this puzzle.
- My 5, 2, 3, 1, 4 is in heaven.
- My 4, 5, 6, 7 is the earth.
- I am a country in Europe.

The Most Challenging "Spider" Puzzle

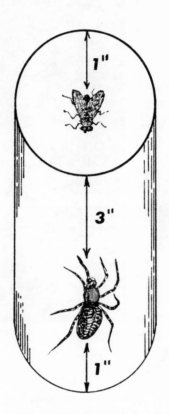

Don't let this problem bug you. In the illustration a glass cylinder is four inches high and six inches in circumference. On the outside of the cylinder is a spider one inch from the bottom, and a fly is on the inside of the cylinder one inch from the top. The spider, on seeing the fly, takes the shortest possible route over the cylinder and pounces on the fly. What route does the spider travel and how many inches does he walk?

The Most Challenging "Earth" Puzzle

The ancient wise man here is working on the old "Steel Band" problem. He put a steel band around the earth at the equator, then cut the band and added ten feet to it. Some magical force now holds the band an equal distance away from the earth. What is this distance? (Assume that the radius of the earth is 4,000 miles and use 3.14 for pi.)

The Most Challenging "Horseshoe" Puzzle

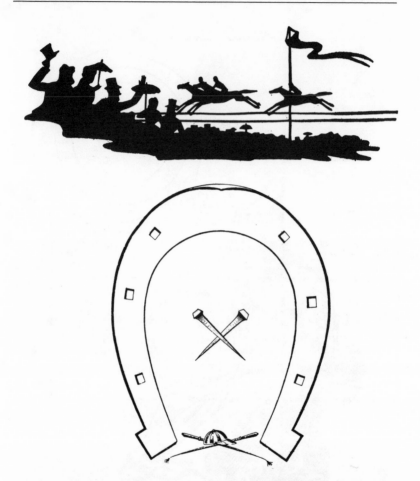

Tallyho, everyone, here's a puzzle you should get a kick out of. Orville Wheelwright, the blacksmith out at the local racecourse, fooled everyone for years with this problem. He would hand you a horseshoe which contained six nail holes and ask you to divide it into six pieces, each piece having one of the nail holes in it, by making only two straight-line cuts across the horseshoe with a hacksaw to accomplish this feat. Care to wager on this one?

The Most Challenging "Rearranging" Puzzle

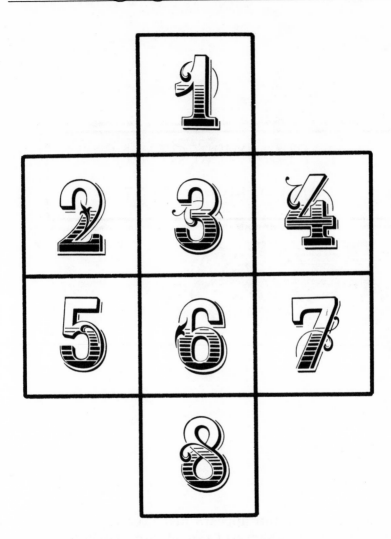

Here's a great puzzle for all of you neatness freaks. All you have to do is arrange the numbers in the boxes above so that no two consecutive numbers are next to each other (horizontally, vertically, or diagonally).

The Most Challenging "Missing Letter" Puzzle

PRSVRYPRFCTMN

VRKPTHSPRCPTSTN

The above inscription appears just over the Ten Commandments in the chancel of a small church in Wales. The addition of a single letter, repeated at various intervals, makes it not only intelligible but appropriate to the situation. What is the missing letter and where does it go in the inscription?

The Most Challenging "Clown" Puzzle

Here are three clowns, John, Dick and Roger. During the winter months each of them has two different vocations. Their six jobs are: truck driver, writer, trumpeter, golf player, computer technician and barber. Given the following six clues, find out the vocations of the three clowns.

- The truck driver flirted with the golf player's sister.
- The trumpeter and the computer technician went horseback riding with John.
- The truck driver laughed at the trumpeter because of his big feet.
- Dick received a box of chocolates from the computer technician.
- The golf player bought a used car from the writer.
- Roger was faster than both Dick and the golf player at eating pizza.

The Most Challenging "Ice-Cream Stick" Puzzle

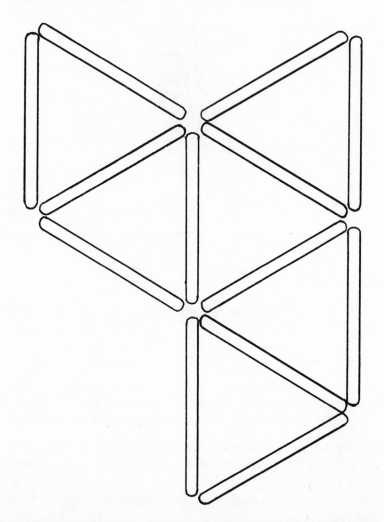

You shouldn't have to try very hard to solve this problem. In the drawing thirteen ice-cream sticks form six equilateral triangles. Can you remove three sticks and have three triangles remaining? Your time limit is three minutes.

The Most Challenging "Archaeology" Puzzle

Those intrepid archaeologists, Petrie and Hawkings, are back at the dig. Hawkings seems to have found another "Find of the Century."

"Petrie, old chap, the men just unearthed this magnificent marble column! I've never seen anything like it! Unfortunately my Latin is rusty and I can't decipher the inscription carved on it. What do you make of it?"

"Hawkings, you never cease to amaze me. It's a fake, of course. Someone has gone to a lot of trouble to pull your leg. Even you should be able to decipher that inscription if you look at it long enough."

Can you help Hawkings with the Mystery of the Monument?

The Most Challenging
"Letter" Puzzle

SPARKLING

Willard Wordsworth, the Word Professor, has a "sparkling" challenge for you. From the word pictured above, see if you can drop one letter so that you have a new word. Then drop another letter, which leaves you with yet another new word. Continue in this fashion until you have dropped out all but one letter, and this last letter should also be a word. At no time can any of the letters be rearranged into a different order when forming each new word. Let's see how polished you are at this type of problem.

The Most Challenging "Riddle" Puzzle

Randolph Rutledge, the Riddle King, has a classic for you to work on. The picture he is pointing to is really a graphic representation of a famous nine-word riddle that asks you to identify an ordinary object that is found around the house. What is the riddle, and what is this elusive object?

The Most Challenging "Counting" Puzzle

Our bold buccaneer is just a-sittin' and a-rockin', waiting for the doldrums to pass so that he can fly his new "puzzle kite." This kite challenges you to figure out how many different-sized squares and triangles are contained in its design. You are allowed only one chance to arrive at the correct totals.

The Most Challenging "Mystery Word" Puzzle

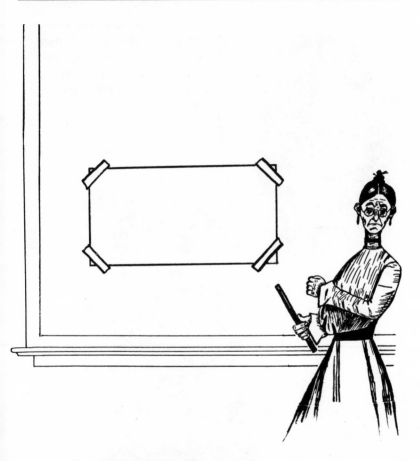

Your favorite substitute teacher, Ms. Priscilla Sunshine, is back for a refresher course in English.

"All right, students, pay attention. Behind this piece of cardboard is a common English word, in use today, that describes a person or a thing as being in no place under the sun, neither here nor there nor anywhere. Yet, if you only add a space between two of its letters, the person or object will be right here at this very moment. Can you tell me what this word is?"

The Most Challenging "Nuptial" Puzzle

"When the day after tomorrow is yesterday; then 'today' will be as far from Sunday as that day was which was 'today' when the day before yesterday was tomorrow."

Obviously the score of this match is Love. The young lady has just asked her fiancé what day of the week he would like to be married on. To say the least, his answer is a little muddled. Can you determine what day of the week he has in mind?

The Most Challenging "Saying" Puzzle

Now, don't get in a stew trying to solve this one. Hidden in the jumble of letters inside the square above the chef's head is a well-known culinary saying. To find it, start with any letter and, reading every other letter, you will find half of the proverb. Then, starting at some other letter, do the same again and you will find the other half. Solve this one in five minutes and you are certainly a seasoned puzzler.

The Most Challenging "Golf" Puzzle

Dashing Dan the Duffer has become the most talked-about player at the Idle Hours Country Club. After years of scooping divots and slicing golf balls through the club-house, Dan has finally gotten his game together. No matter what club he uses, the ball travels only one of two distances. Dan has worked it out so that by combining these two shots, sometimes hitting two long shots and one short shot, for example, he can play the front nine of the course in 26 strokes. He always plays in a straight line from tee to cup, since his hooks and slices are a thing of the past. Occasionally he hits the ball past the green but he always chips back to hole out. It makes no difference to him because he is always able to sink the ball by hitting it one of two distances. Our problem is: What are the two distances that Dan uses in hitting his way to fame and fortune? Keep in mind that Dan's yardage for the first nine holes is 150 yards, 300 yards, 250 yards, 325 yards, 275 yards, 350 yards, 225 yards, 400 yards, and 425 yards.

The Most Challenging "Flatland" Puzzle

Our local silhouette artist has cut us a pretty problem. With pencil and paper, duplicate the design in the picture being held up by the two young ladies. You must use one continuous line; you cannot lift the pencil off the paper or go over any part of the line more than once; and the continuous line cannot cross itself at any point.

The Most Challenging "Alphabet" Puzzle

It's testing time at the ABC Puzzle and Game Company again. The boss loves to give out bonuses, but you have to solve puzzles to get them. This week's puzzle is worth $10. Let's see if you earn it. Above and below the line is printed a portion of the alphabet, with some of the letters above the line and some below. Write the remaining letters of the alphabet, placing them correctly either above or below the line according to the boss's hidden scheme.

The Most Challenging "Clock" Puzzle

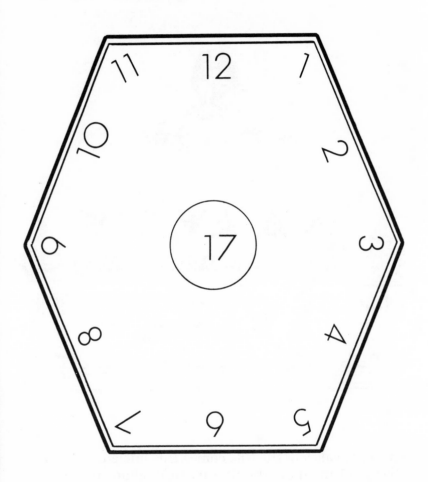

Here's a timeless problem. The municipal building recently had a new clock installed with a very modern face. The next night, a local wag climbed up and rearranged the numbers on the face so that the sum of the three numbers on each of the six sides totalled seventeen. Now, how did he manage that? Don't go cuckoo trying to solve this one.

The Most Challenging "Pyramid" Puzzle

From the valley of the Nile comes this ancient and venerable problem. Above the altar in the diagram are six pyramids. The problem is to rearrange them so that they will be positioned as shown under the altar. The rules for effecting this change are as follows: You only have three moves; you must move two *adjacent* pyramids during each move; a move is considered turning a pyramid end for end; and each pyramid must remain in the same spot. May the power of the pyramid be with you!

The Most Challenging "Poker Chip" Puzzle

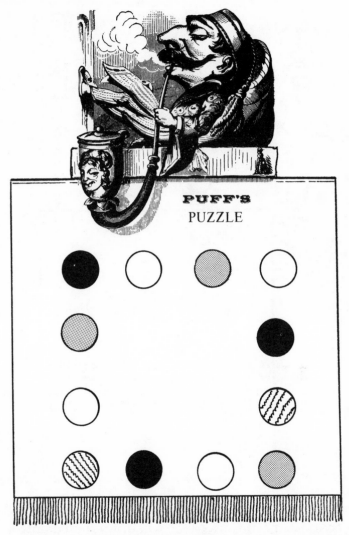

PUFF'S
PUZZLE

Mr. Puff has an interesting little puzzle. Lay out twelve poker chips in the form of a square, with four chips to a side. Now rearrange the twelve chips so that there are five chips on each side of the square.

The Most Challenging "College Boy" Puzzle

Dear Dad;

$$S E N D$$
$$+ M O R E$$
$$\overline{M O N E Y}$$

Love

Jr.

"Send more money," the cry of the impoverished college student—a cry that this time will be answered only if his father can decipher the message. Each letter of the message represents a digit—zero through nine. Some of the letters are used more than once. How much, in dollars and cents, does Junior need?

The Most Challenging "Statue" Puzzle

"*With thieves I consort,*
With the vilest, in short,
  I'm quite at my ease in depravity;
Yet all divines use me,
And savants can't lose me,
  For I am the center of gravity."

The Kitchen Sink

The Kitchen Sink here is an example of a Talking Puzzle Statue. This rare and exotic art form has a repertoire of over 100 puzzles. Let's see if you can figure out to the letter this Delphic utterance.

The Most Challenging "Punctuation" Puzzle

"Quimby, you call yourself a proof-reader? Just look at this quotation from Professor Stoic's address last night! You left out all of the punctuation!"

THAT THAT IS IS THAT THAT IS NOT IS NOT IS THAT IT THAT IS IT

Above is Professor Stoic's quotation without any punctuation. Can you bring order out of this academic chaos with the proper addition of a few commas, a period or two, and perhaps a question mark for emphasis?

The Most Challenging "Milk Bottle" Puzzle

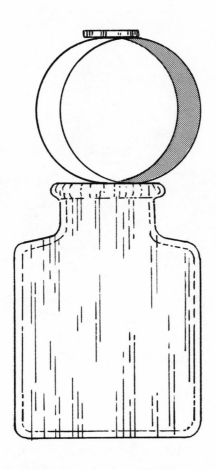

Form a one-inch-wide loop of stiff paper. Place this loop on top of an empty bottle or glass jar. On top of the loop, directly over the mouth of the bottle, place a dime. Your problem is to get the dime into the bottle by only touching the paper loop. You are also only allowed to use one hand while solving the puzzle.

The Most Challenging "Soup Tureen" Puzzle

Aunt Edna always kept a large amount of money around her house for emergencies. The only trouble was that she never trusted paper money; so her hoard became quite bulky. She also hid her savings in the most unlikely of places—a silver soup tureen. When she counted her money she found the most extraordinary coincidence. She had exactly $700, divided equally into quarters, half-dollars, and silver dollars. Can you tell how many of each there were?

The Most Challenging "Bug" Puzzle

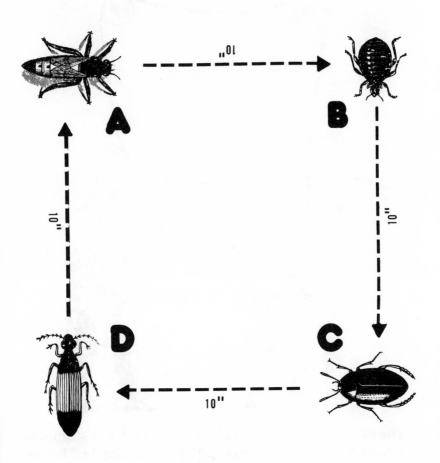

Four bugs were positioned on top of a table. Each bug was exactly ten inches away from the bug that it was facing. If each bug started crawling simultaneously, and at a constant speed, towards the bug that it faced (A towards B, B towards C, C towards D, and D towards A), what distance had each bug traveled when they all met?

The Most Challenging "Bell" Puzzle

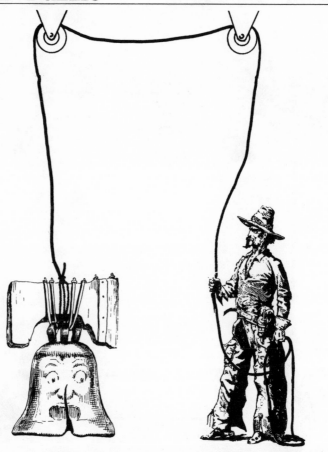

The Reverend I. N. Spire is back for a last try at stumping you. It seems the Reverend purchased a new bell for his church, and somehow he was able to talk the Durango Kid into helping him hang it. The bell and the Kid weighed the same. When the Kid started hauling on the rope a surprising thing happened. See if you can guess if . . .

- the bell went up while the Kid stayed down?
- the Kid went up while the bell stayed down?
- the Kid and the bell went up together?

The Most Challenging "Hunter" Puzzle

Twice four and twenty blackbirds
   Were sitting in the rain;
I shot and killed a seventh part,
   How many did remain?

   The above bit of verse offers us an old and interesting puzzle to think over. Can you answer the question propounded here by Sir Blunder Buss?

The Most Challenging "Bishop" Puzzle

We've already heard from a reverend, and now it's time to give the bishops a turn. Our problem is a straightforward one. Figure out what is the maximum number of bishops that can be placed on a chessboard so that no bishop is in a position to capture any other bishop. The color of the pieces makes no difference. Remember that in chess a bishop can only move in a diagonal direction.

The Most Challenging "Castle" Puzzle

Many years ago, an elderly king, his son and daughter, weighing 195 pounds, 105 pounds, and 90 pounds, respectively, were kept prisoners at the top of a high tower in Grimsley Castle. The only communication with the ground below was a cord passing over a pulley with a basket at each end. When one basket rested on the ground the other was opposite the window. Naturally, if one basket was more heavily loaded than the other, the heavier would descend; but if the excess on either side was more than fifteen pounds, the descent would become dangerous, because it would be so rapid that none of the prisoners could control it. The only thing available to help them in the tower was a cannonball, weighing 75 pounds. Still, they managed to escape. How did they do it? (Our thanks go out to Professor Hoffmann, who wrote this puzzle over a hundred years ago in his great book, *Puzzles Old and New*.)

The Most Challenging "Square" Puzzle

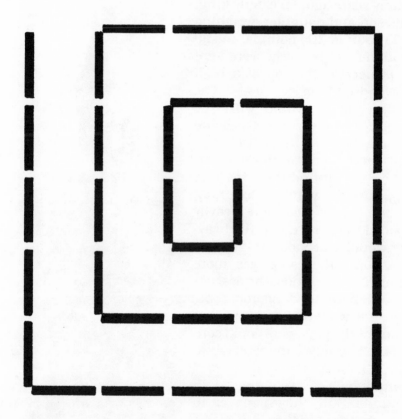

You're going to love fooling your friends with this one. Lay out 35 pencils in the spiral shown here. Now, challenge anyone to move four of the pencils to new positions so that three perfect squares are formed.

The Most Challenging "Presidents" Puzzle

Either the little girl here is trying to hurry Christmas along or she is looking for the answer to the famous Presidents Puzzle. See if you can solve it so that she can concentrate on important matters. The problem is to determine what two dates, between the presidencies of Ulysses S. Grant and Gerald R. Ford, read the same upside down as they do right side up.

The Most Challenging "Checkers" Puzzle

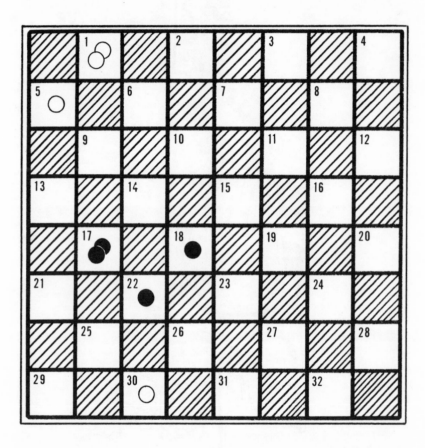

A few pages ago we had a chess problem; now the game is checkers. This is one of those old-fashioned problems where you have to contrive the winning strategy. It's Black's turn to go. If he makes the right move, the game is in the bag. What should he do?

The Most Challenging "Web" Puzzle

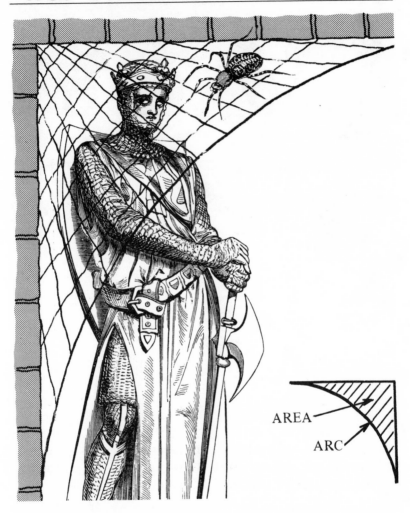

AREA

ARC

A statue stands in a gloomy alcove in Grimsley Castle. Partly blocking the entrance is a giant spider's web. The arc of the web is exactly one quarter of a circle and is twenty inches long. Given these facts, can you calculate the area covered by the web in square inches without getting caught in this problem?

The Most Challenging "Dictionary" Puzzle

A. sou'wester   E. vestee   I. farthingale   M. harlequin
B. barrow   F. auk   J. biretta   N. gemsbok
C. hoplite   G. caryatid K. minaret   O. autogiro
D. campanile   H. puffin   L. zebu   P. toby
                                                   Q. cockle

For those of you who enjoy word puzzles we present the old dictionary quiz. Above are illustrations taken from a very old dictionary. Below are listed seventeen words, twelve of which describe the illustrated items. Can you match them up?

The Most Challenging "Bridge" Puzzle

Now, here's a good way to win a dinner the next time you're out with some friends. Put two glasses on the table a short distance apart and place a sheet of fairly stiff paper across the tops of the glasses. Next, state that you have the power to hypnotize the paper and make it strong enough to support a third glass placed in the middle of the paper. This puzzle is a good stumper, but give it a try before heading out to the restaurant.

The Most Challenging
"Wineglass" Puzzle

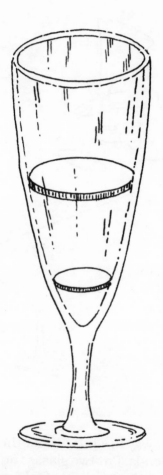

You'll need a good thinking cap to solve this one. Place a dime and a half-dollar in a small wineglass as shown above. Your problem is to remove the dime from the glass without touching either the glass or the half-dollar. Now, this is what I call a hard problem!

The Most Challenging "Bottle and Keg" Puzzle

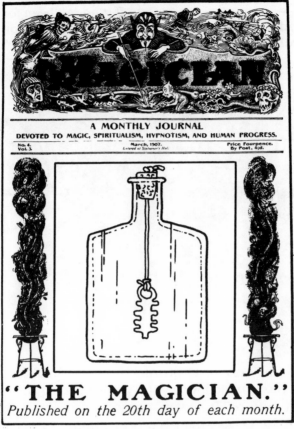

A MONTHLY JOURNAL

DEVOTED TO MAGIC, SPIRITUALISM, HYPNOTISM, AND HUMAN PROGRESS.

No. 4.
Vol. 5.

March, 1907.
Entered at Stationer's Hal.

Price Fourpence.
By Post, 4½d.

"THE MAGICIAN."

Published on the 20th day of each month.

Framed in the cover of a fascinating old magic magazine is an equally fascinating old puzzle. Tie a key to the end of a piece of string; then pass the other end of the string through a hole that has been drilled in a piece of cork. After knotting the end of the string, lower the key into the bottle and place the cork firmly into the neck of the bottle. Your challenge, if you wish to accept it, is to remove the key from the string without touching the cork, the string, the bottle or the table that it is standing on. You're going to need a genie to help you solve this one.

The Most Challenging "Horse" Puzzle

"I say, did you hear about the Tralawny will mix-up?"

"If it hadn't been for that lawyer chap, Trevor Torts, they'd still be at it!"

During the Annual Costume Hunting Breakfast at the Tallyho Club the following story was making the rounds:

When Squire Tralawny passed away, he left a will whereby he bequeathed his best jumping horses to his three sons, John, James, and William. The bequest was to be divided in the following manner: John, the eldest, was to receive half, James was to have a third, and William a ninth of the stable. When he died, however, it was found that the number of horses in the stable was seventeen, a number which was divisible neither by two, three, or nine. In their perplexity the three brothers consulted a clever lawyer, who hit on a scheme whereby the Squire's intentions were carried out to the satisfaction of all parties. How was it managed?

The Most Challenging "Counterfeit Coin" Puzzle

This problem was used in the Annual Puzzle Club elimination contest.

On a table were ten hats numbered from one to ten. Inside each hat were ten gold coins. The coins all looked alike, but those in one of the hats were all counterfeit. The real coins weighed ten grams apiece, while each counterfeit coin weighed nine grams. To help the contestants solve the problem a scale was provided that gave weights in grams. However, the contestants could only use this scale once. They could, however, place as many coins into the scale as they wished for this one weighing. Given these facts, which hat contained the bogus bullion?

The Most Challenging "Ancient Coin" Puzzle

The fair lady shown here is contemplating the three ancient coins brought home to her by a suitor who had recently sojourned on the subcontinent of India. While there, an Indian prince presented him with the coins and a problem to go along with them: "It is written that on the road to Bombay two fathers and two sons found 3 rupees (silver coins). Without delay they divided them up, each receiving one coin." How was this possible?

The Most Challenging "Scholar" Puzzle

First Scholar: "Drat, I can't find the answer in any of these books. Please read that puzzle to me again."

Second Scholar: "Now, let me see. Oh, yes, here it is: 'Take away my first letter and I remain unchanged; take away my second letter and I remain unchanged; take away my third letter and I remain unchanged; take away all my letters and still I remain exactly the same.' "

First Scholar: "What in the world could the word be?"

The Most Challenging "Automobile" Puzzle

Here's a puzzle from the Roaring Twenties. When a car is in motion, does the upper part of each wheel move faster than the part of each wheel nearest the ground? Since a wheel is a solid object that revolves around a central point, any two points on the wheel, each of which is the same distance from the hub, must move at the same rate of speed. If, in fact, both points move at the same rate of speed, then they should cover the same distance during a given period of time.

"Oh, yeah," said young Stanley Steamer, "then how do you explain the fact that when you look at the wheel of a passing car the spokes in the upper half of the wheel seem to be blurred while the spokes in the bottom half can clearly be seen and even counted if the car is moving slowly enough. Is this an optical illusion, or is the top half of the wheel really moving faster than the bottom half?"

What do you think? Do points *a* and *b*, marked on the top and bottom of the front tire, travel at the same rate of speed, or does one of them travel faster than the other?

The Most Challenging "Shield" Puzzle

Our next problem comes from ancient Babylon. The shield is encircled by twelve black dots. The problem is to place eleven coins on eleven of these dots according to the following instructions: Starting at any dot, count six dots and place a coin on the sixth dot. Always count in a clockwise direction. Starting at another empty dot, count around the circle and place another coin on an empty dot. Continue this until all of the coins have been placed on different dots. When counting, treat a dot with a coin on it like an empty dot and count it along with the rest. Remember, you must always start counting at an empty dot.

The Most Challenging "Trick" Puzzle

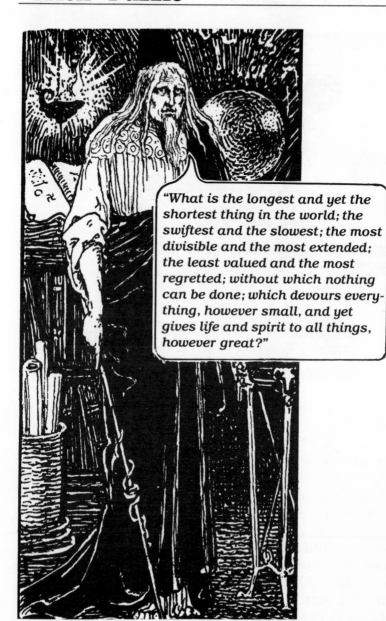

"What is the longest and yet the shortest thing in the world; the swiftest and the slowest; the most divisible and the most extended; the least valued and the most regretted; without which nothing can be done; which devours everything, however small, and yet gives life and spirit to all things, however great?"

The Most Challenging "Door" Puzzle

While admiring a new door donated to his college, Willard Wordsworth was inspired to create a new puzzle. "Students," he challenged, "I want you to rearrange the letters in the two words *new door* to make one word." You have until the bell sounds to turn in your answer.

The Most Challenging "Samurai" Puzzle

This samurai swordsman might well be singing that old song, "There's a long, long trail a-winding . . ." as he contemplates the castle of his old army buddy perched on top of Mount Foolisama. Now, Mount Foolisama is in the shape of a perfectly circular cone: It measures two kilometres across at the circular base and stands exactly one kilometre high above the plain below. A long path ascends counterclockwise from the base of the mountain to the castle at the top. The path winds around and around, with a slope of one metre in ten, with the spiral getting ever tighter. How far does the samurai have to travel, from base to peak, before he can have a martial arts workout with his old army buddy?

The Most Challenging "Eight Word" Puzzle

crabcake   stupid

laughing   hijack

calmness   first

canopy   deft

What do the above eight words have in common?

The Most Challenging "Train" Puzzle

One day, on the old Erie Lackawanna railroad line, two passenger trains were hurtling towards one another (on parallel tracks, fortunately). The train out of Morristown was heading east at a breathtaking six miles an hour, while the other train, out of Hoboken, was heading west at a steady four miles an hour. Somewhere outside of Maplewood, when the trains were exactly a half mile apart, a horsefly that had been dozing on the Hoboken locomotive decided that it was time for a little exercise. He flew off at the rate of twenty miles an hour straight for the oncoming train from Morristown. As soon as he reached it, he turned around and flew back to the engine from Hoboken. He kept this up, darting back and forth between engines, until the two trains met, at which point he alighted once again on the Hoboken train and went back to sleep. Assuming that the horsefly maintained a constant rate of twenty miles per hour what distance did it cover during its flight?

The Most Challenging "Mental" Puzzle

Punch is expressing himself rather freely concerning his thoughts on this puzzle. He had to add up all of the numbers from one to 100 in his head. After working ten minutes on the problem he gave up, complaining that he kept losing track of which number he had added last. What Punch didn't know was that there is a simple solution to this problem that would allow him to solve it in twenty seconds or less. Can you discover what this solution is?

The Most Challenging "Hand" Puzzle

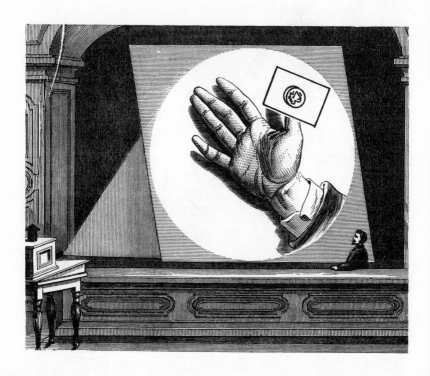

Balance a playing card horizontally on the top of your right thumb. Now lay a coin (a half dollar or a quarter) on it so that both are steady. Now comes the hard part. Remove the card without touching the coin. The coin should remain balanced on the thumb. You'll get a real hand if you can solve this the first time out.

The Most Challenging "Quarter" Puzzle

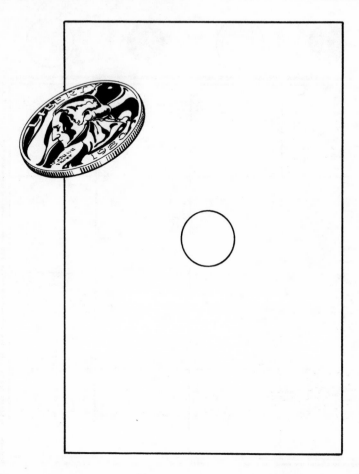

Here's another "betcha"-type puzzle. In a piece of stout paper cut a circular hole the size of a nickel. Invite anyone to pass a quarter through the hole without mutilating the coin or tearing the paper. They will naturally tell you that it can't be done, the diameter of the quarter being so much greater than that of the hole. And yet the impossible is possible. Can you figure out the solution to this tight squeeze?

The Most Challenging "Five and Ten Cent" Puzzle

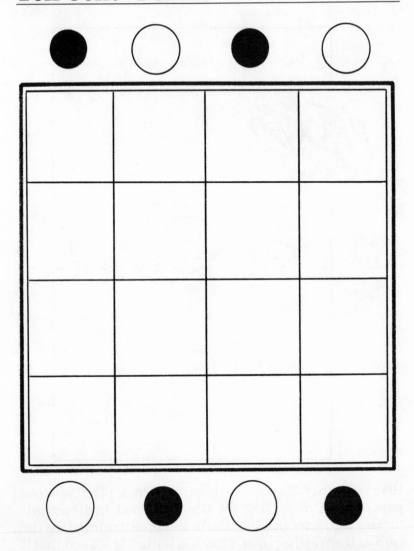

Place four nickels and four dimes in the sixteen squares in such a way that no two coins of the same denomination will be in the same row, horizontally, vertically, or diagonally. Be careful; it's not as easy as it looks.

ANSWERS

"Geometry" puzzle (page 6). Lines *BD*, *DG* and *GB* form an equilateral triangle. Therefore, the angle between lines *BD* and *DG* is 60°.

"Coffee" puzzle (page 7). Mr. Fussbudget knew it was the same cup of coffee that he had sent back because he had put sugar in the cup before he discovered the fly swimming in it. When he took a sip of the returned cup he immediately detected the sweetness.

"Tombstone" puzzle (page 8). According to the inscription Mrs. Sarah Fountain died before her husband. If this were so, how then could she have been his widow?

"Magic Square" puzzle (page 9).

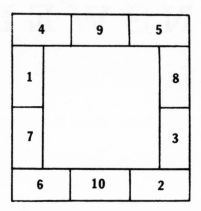

"Tennis Ball" puzzle (page 10). Harriet gets the club grounds keeper, Thaddeus Rackencut, to fill the hole with water from a nearby hose and the tennis ball promptly floats to the top. Game, set and match if you figured this one out.

"Thimble" puzzle (page 11). The secret is quite simple. Always place the next thimble on a point that will allow you to slide it along to the point of the star your last thimble started from. For example: place the thimble on point *W* and slide it over to point *X*; then place the next thimble on point *Y* and slide it along to point *W*. Next, place a thimble on point *Z* and slide it over to point *Y*. Continue in this manner until all of the seven thimbles are in place.

"Chalk" puzzle (page 12). The picture looks down at the seven pieces of chalk assembled for the solution. The circle in the middle is the end of one piece of chalk, seen head-on. There are two groups of three pieces each, each group on top of one another, placed around this central piece of chalk. On close examination it will be seen that every piece touches every other piece. Thanks to Martin Gardner for this outstanding puzzle.

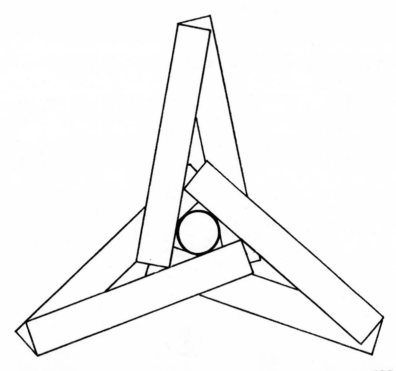

"Bakery" puzzle (page 13). The horizontal cut shown here will nicely divide the poppy seed loaf into ten pieces. The pieces are not all the same size or shape, but there is enough for everyone to have a taste.

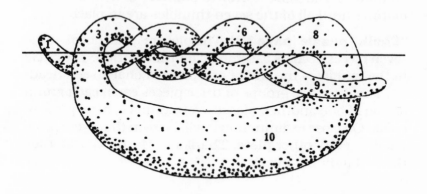

"Goblet" puzzle (page 14). Take the coin and wedge it between the middle tines of both forks; then place the back edge of the coin on the rim of the glass and adjust the forks backwards towards the glass until the coin is balanced. It's really very easy.

"Bicycle" puzzle (page 15). Against the wind he could pedal 15 miles in an hour. With the wind he could pedal 20 miles in an hour. The difference is 5 miles an hour. Half of this is 2.5 miles. Therefore, the velocity of the wind was 2.5 miles per hour. So, on a calm day he could pedal 17.5 miles per hour, the difference between 15 miles and 20 miles.

$$\frac{60 \text{ minutes}}{17.5 \text{ miles}} = \frac{3,600 \text{ seconds}}{17.50 \text{ miles}} = 205.7 \text{ seconds per mile}$$

$$= 3 \text{ minutes } 26 \text{ seconds}$$
per mile on a calm day.

"Match" puzzle (page 16). Move the two matches, indicated by the dash lines, to the new positions pointed to by the arrows. You now have four squares.

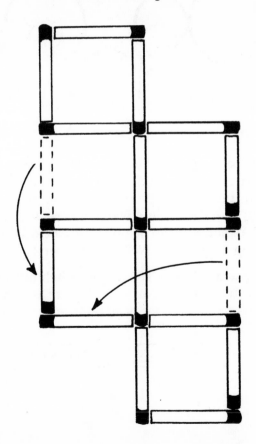

"Coin" puzzle (page 17). Place the forefinger of your left hand firmly on the middle coin (the coin that can be touched but not moved). With your right hand move the quarter on the right a few inches away from the nickel (the coin that can be touched or moved). Now bring this quarter back smartly against the nickel. The nickel will not move, but the impact will cause the quarter on the left of the nickel to move away two or three inches from the nickel, thus creating an opening between them that you can now move the right-hand quarter into. Problem solved!

"Egg" puzzle (page 18). For those who have to poach the answer, here goes: Turn both sand timers over at the same time. When the sand in the three-minute timer runs out, pop the egg into the boiling water. There is still two minutes' worth of sand in the five-minute clock. When it runs out, your egg is finished. Well done, Albert!

"Magnet" puzzle (page 19). If you touch one end of one bar against the end of the other bar, there is an attraction, but you can't tell which bar is attracting the other (Fig. 1).

| magnet | non–magnet |

FIG.1

However, if you touch the end of one bar against the middle of the other bar the following happens: If the bar being touched against the middle of the other bar is the magnet, it attracts the other bar (Fig. 2). If, on the other hand, it is not the magnet, it doesn't attract the other bar because a bar magnet has almost no attracting power at its center (Fig. 3). Thus, if the touching bar is a magnet, it attracts, and if it is not a magnet, there is no visible attraction.

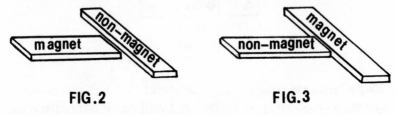

FIG. 2   **FIG. 3**

"Glass" puzzle (page 20). Use a heavy glass when you practise this trick. Place the thumb and forefinger of one hand on both coins and smartly snap them down against the sides of the glass (Fig. 1). Next, move the coins down to the middle of the glass (Fig. 2). Now for the finish: Pull the coins off the glass with a snapping motion (Fig. 3). This puzzle ought to keep you in free lemonade.

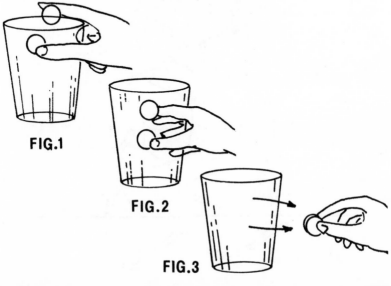

FIG.1

FIG.2

FIG.3

"Card" puzzle (page 21). Place the four cards together as shown, with the upper right-hand corner of each card overlapped by the card above it.

"Rope" puzzle (page 22). The secret to this Eastern mystery is to cross your arms before bending down to pick up the ends of the rope. Once you have an end in each hand unfold your arms and the knot appears magically in the middle of the rope. And you never let go of the ends while doing it! Amazing!

"Soda Bottle" puzzle (page 23). Note the wording of the challenge carefully—it states that you will put "a half-dollar" into a bottle, not that you will put the half-dollar on the table into the bottle. Take a paper dollar and tear it in half; then roll up one half of the bill and shove it into the bottle, thus fulfilling your earlier claim of being able to do the impossible. (One key point about this solution is that you really put a half-dollar into the bottle and not five dimes or ten nickels, as some might claim as an alternate solution to the problem.)

"Area" puzzle (page 24). The shaded area is one quarter of the area of the three-inch square. Since the area of the square is nine square inches, then the shaded area must be 2¼ square inches. You can rotate the four-inch square to any other position around the smaller square and the area covered will always remain the same, 2¼ square inches. If you rotate the larger square to bisect line *ac*, it will then cover an area on the smaller square measuring 1½ inches by 1½ inches, exactly 2¼ square inches.

"Milk Train" puzzle (page 25). He shipped the cows.

"Lunch" puzzle (page 26). He won by losing the bet! Treadmill picked up the basket and ate the boss's $6.00 triple-decker sandwich down to the last pickle. When he was finished, he gave the boss 50¢ and said, "I should have known better than to have wagered with you, Sir. You're a tough man to beat."

"Scissors" puzzle (page 27). Take hold of the loop behind the string in the left bow of the scissors and gently pull on it. As it gets longer, slip it through the back right bow, keeping it behind the string that is already through it. Continue pulling on the loop until it is long enough for you to slip the point of the scissors through it. Now let go of the loop and pull the string free of the scissors. Make sure that while you're lengthening the loop, you do not twist it around on itself. That would only cause the scissors to become further ensnared on the string.

"Rectangle" puzzle (page 28). Place the four rectangles together as shown. Note that the ends of the pieces make up the sides of an empty one-inch square formed in the middle (shaded area).

		1 X 1	
1 X 3			1 X 4
		1 X 2	

"Cord" puzzle (page 29). Sir Goodwin retrieved all 160 feet of the Golden Cords and brought them safely back to England, where they provided for him in his old age. Here's how he did it. First, he took the two ends at the bottom and tied them tightly together (Fig. 1). Next, he climbed up the rope on the left until he reached the top. There he wrapped his legs around both pieces of rope and, while hanging on for dear life, he cut the right-hand rope free with his dagger. He then took the end of the right-hand rope and

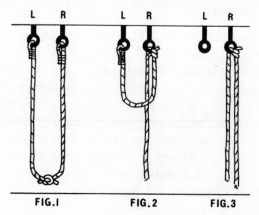

FIG. I   FIG. 2   FIG. 3

poked it back through the ring that had originally held it. He kept pulling the rope through until the knotted ends reached the ring (Fig. 2). Taking hold of the doubled rope that now hung from the right-hand ring, Sir Goodwin shifted around and cut the cord on the left side free from its supporting ring (Fig. 3). Sir Goodwin then carefully slid down the doubled cord to the floor. Once there, he pulled the cords free of the ring and hightailed it for home.

"Four-Letter Word" puzzle (page 30). As far as four-letter words go, the Dutchman had a clean vocabulary. The only English word that fits his puzzle is *NOON*.

"Number" puzzle (page 31). The selling of "products" was Distin's game and so is the solution to this puzzle. Each number is the product of the digits that make up the preceding number: 49 equals 7 times 7; 36 equals 4 times 9; and 18 equals 3 times 6. Therefore, the answer to our problem is 8 equals 1 times 8. A thumping good problem!

"Star" puzzle (page 32).

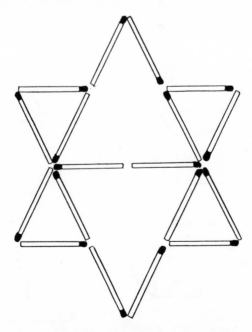

"Frat" puzzle (page 33). This rebus puzzle is probably 100 years old and is the work of that master puzzler, Sam Loyd. Here's his answer: He is not a young man because he is *over forty*. He is a scholar because he is *intent on his letters*. Finally, he is smart because he is *bound to excel*.

"Salt and Pepper" puzzle (page 34). It helps to have a full head of hair for this puzzle. Take your comb and run it several times through your hair. Now lower it down so that the teeth are right above the specks of pepper. Miraculously, the pepper will leap from the salt and will cling to the magnetically charged comb, thanks to the charge of static electricity you imparted to it when you ran it through your locks. Judging by Herbert's thinning top, I'd say that he won't be doing this mystery much longer.

"Pencil" puzzle (page 35).

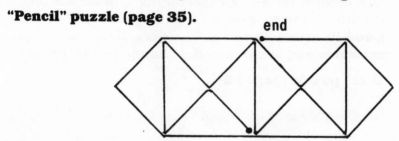

"Block" puzzle (page 36). Here are the eight possible constructions.

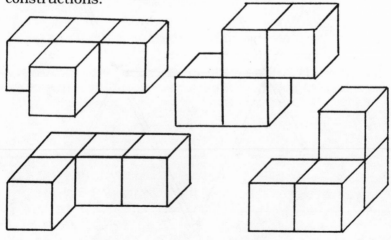

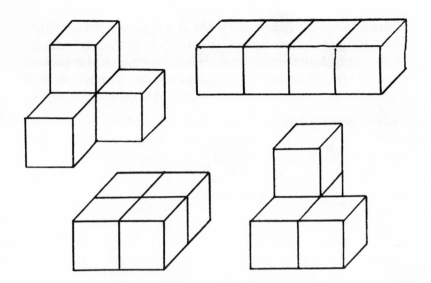

"Theatre" puzzle (page 37). The breakdown of the admissions was: 11 men paid $55.00; 19 women paid $38.00; and 70 children paid $7.00—all told, a total of exactly $100.00 and 100 people.

"Age" puzzle (page 38). We know that Joan has 3 children and that the product of their ages is 36. Fred says that he needs more information and he is right. The combinations of ages that give a product of 36 are: $3 \times 3 \times 4 = 36$, $36 \times 1 \times 1 = 36$, $12 \times 3 \times 1 = 36$, $2 \times 2 \times 9 = 36$, $6 \times 3 \times 2 = 36$, $6 \times 6 \times 1 = 36$, $9 \times 4 \times 1 = 36$, and $18 \times 2 \times 1 = 36$. Next, she gives the clue that the sum of their ages is the same as her street address, which he knows. Since he says that he needs still more information, it must mean that more than one of the combinations add up to the same street number. The only duplicates from the aforementioned combinations are $6 + 6 + 1 = 13$ and $2 + 2 + 9 = 13$. But which one is the right combination? The third clue gives Fred the answer. His dancing partner tells him that the "oldest *one* likes tennis." This eliminates $6 + 6 + 1$ because there would be "two" oldest children there. So, the correct answer is, "Joan has three children, ages 9, 2 and 2." This problem is child's play to solve.

"Sting" puzzle (page 39). Okay, here's the sting. Turn over the quarter and place it on top of a "heads" nickel. Make sure that the quarter completely hides the nickel. Now, if you look at the table, you'll see that there is only 40¢ in heads showing. That's a honey of a puzzle.

"Vase" puzzle (page 40). Cut the vase along lines *A* and *B*. Rearrange the three pieces to form the square depicted by the dotted lines.

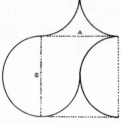

"Fish" puzzle (page 41).

"3-D" puzzle (page 42). The numbers will aid in explaining how the line is drawn. Remember that some parts of the continuous line go behind other parts of the same line. Let's start: Go from point 1 to 5 to 6 to 2 to 10 to 1 to 3 to 7 to 9 to 3 to 4 to 8 to 7 to 5 to 10 to 6 to 8 to 9 to 4 to 2 to 1. When you are finished, you will have perfectly duplicated the above cubes without once having crossed the line over itself (three-dimensionally speaking, of course).

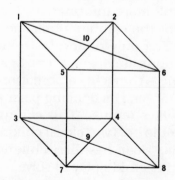

"Buzz Saw" puzzle (page 43). The least number of pieces is two. Cut out the piece outlined by the dotted line, turn it end for end, and replace it in the board. The hole is now in the middle of the board.

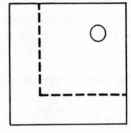

"Light" puzzle (page 44). He should light the match first.

"Word" puzzle (page 45). 1. Soap box 2. Circles under eyes 3. Backward glance 4. I understand 5. Zero degrees 6. Upper crust.

"Perception" puzzle (page 46). The answer is that six F's are in the sentence. Why it's so difficult to count them the first time is hard to say. People seem to miss the F's in the "of's". Try this one on your friends and see how they do.

"Country" puzzle (page 47). The answers to the first four hints are: END, GLAD, ANGEL and LAND. The answer to the charade is ENGLAND.

"Spider" puzzle (page 48). To illustrate the solution imagine the cylinder opened out flat. The location of the fly is point *F* and the location of the spider is point *S*. Now

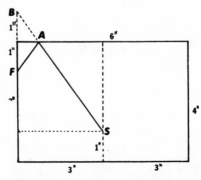

extend the line of the left side upwards one inch to point B. Line BS cuts the top edge of the drawing at point A, the point where the spider goes over the edge of the cylinder. The spider's route is the hypotenuse of a right triangle with a base four inches long, and a high side three inches long. Thus, the hypotenuse has to be five inches long, the shortest route that the spider can take.

"Earth" puzzle (page 49). In the following equations $C =$ circumference; $r =$ radius; and $\pi = 3.14$ (r_1 is the radius of the earth; r_2 is the radius of the steel band):

$$C = 2\pi r_1 \qquad C + 10 = 2\pi r_2$$

$$r_1 = \frac{C}{2\pi} \qquad r_2 = \frac{C + 10}{2\pi}$$

$$r_1 = 4,000 \quad r_2 - r_1 = \frac{C + 10}{2\pi} - \frac{C}{2\pi} = \frac{10}{2\pi} = \frac{5}{\pi}$$

$$r_2 - r_1 = 1.59 \text{ FEET}$$

"Horseshoe" puzzle (page 50). Make your first cut along line 1–1; then take the top piece of the shoe (a) and place it on top of piece c. Now make cut 2–2. You will then have six pieces, each with a nail hole in it.

"Rearranging" puzzle (page 51).

"Missing Letter" puzzle (page 52). Insert the letter *E* at the proper intervals, and it makes the inscription read as follows:

PERSEVERE YE PERFECT MEN,
EVER KEEP THESE PRECEPTS TEN

"Clown" puzzle (page 53). John is the golf player and the barber. Dick is the trumpeter and the writer. Roger is the computer technician and the truck driver.

"Ice-Cream Stick" puzzle (page 54). All you have to do is remove three of the inner ice-cream sticks. After all, it doesn't say that the remaining triangles have to all be of the same size.

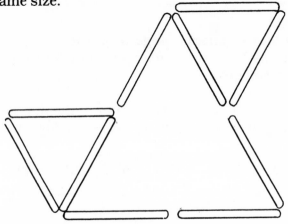

"Archaeology" puzzle (page 55). If you write the letters out in the order in which they appear on the monument, then place spaces in the proper places to form words, you get in English, not Latin, the inscription "TO TIE HORSES TO." In other words, Hawkings has unearthed a fake hitching post for horses.

"Letter" puzzle (page 56). The words are formed in the following order: *SPARKLING, SPARKING, SPARING, SPRING, SPRIG, PRIG, PIG, PI, I.*

"Riddle" puzzle (page 57). The riddle is "What is black and white and red (read) all over?" The answer to the riddle is "a newspaper."

"Counting" puzzle (page 58). There are 34 squares and 104 triangles of several different sizes in the kite. Many of the squares and triangles overlap parts of other squares and triangles. Here are the different sizes of both figures as they appear in our drawing.

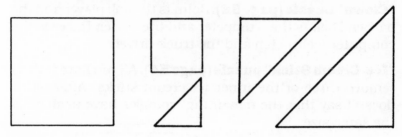

"Mystery Word" puzzle (page 59). The word that Ms. Sunshine has in mind is *nowhere*. Put a space in its middle and you get *now here*.

"Nuptial" puzzle (page 60). The day of the nuptials will be Sunday. You have to break the solution down into two parts.

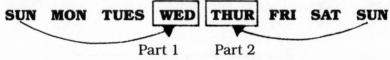

In Part 1 ("When the day after tomorrow is yesterday, then 'today' will be as far from Sunday . . ."), going from Sunday forward, we arrive at Wednesday, 3 days away. In Part 2 (". . . as that day was which was 'today' when the day before yesterday was tomorrow."), going from Sunday backwards, we arrive at Thursday, which is also 3 days away from Sunday. The answer, of course, has to be the day of the week given in the problem.

"Saying" puzzle (page 61). Start at the *A* on the right side of the square. Going around clockwise, and reading every other letter, you get A WATCHED POT. After the word POT, start again with the letter *N*, also on the right side of the square, and reading every other letter, you get NEVER

BOILS. Thus, our kitchen klassic is A WATCHED POT NEVER BOILS, but many a puzzler does when trying to solve this one.

"Golf" puzzle (page 62). Dashing Dan's two shots are a 150-yard drive and a 125-yard approach shot. The holes are made in the following manner: 150 yards: 1 drive. 300 yards: 2 drives. 250 yards: 2 approaches. 325 yards: 3 drives, 1 approach back. 275 yards: 1 drive, 1 approach. 350 yards: 4 approaches, 1 drive back. 225 yards: 3 approaches, 1 drive back. 400 yards: 1 drive, 2 approaches. 425 yards: 2 drives, 1 approach.

"Flatland" puzzle (page 63).

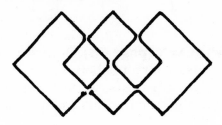

"Alphabet" puzzle (page 64). The answer to the boss's bonus puzzle is:

A   EF HI KLMN   T VWXYZ
BCD G J   OPQRS U

All the letters made with straight lines are above the line while the letters made with curved lines are below the line. Now, everyone entitled to a bonus take two steps forward.

"Clock" puzzle (page 65).

"Pyramid" puzzle (page 66). First invert pyramids 2 and 3; then invert pyramids 3 and 4, and finally, invert pyramids 4 and 5.

"Poker Chip" puzzle (page 67). Rearrange the chips as shown so that there are two chips at every corner of the square. Each side of the square now contains five chips.

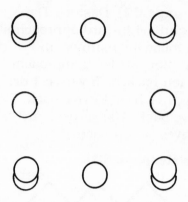

"College Boy" puzzle (page 68). Substituting the numbers for the letters in our alphabetic equation, and adding a decimal point for the cents, we find that Junior needs exactly $106.52, the sum that his dad quickly dispatched to him.

$$
\begin{array}{r}
\text{SEND} \\
+\text{MORE} \\
\hline
\text{MONEY}
\end{array}
\quad = \quad
\begin{array}{r}
9567 \\
+1085 \\
\hline
10652
\end{array}
$$

"Statue" puzzle (page 69). The answer to this wonderful puzzle is the letter *V*. If you look back at the six lines that make up the puzzle, you will see that the letter *V* appears in each of six words: thieves, vilest, depravity, divines, savants and gravity.

"Punctuation" puzzle (page 70). The following punctuation brings order out of chaos: THAT THAT IS, IS. THAT THAT IS NOT, IS NOT. IS THAT IT? THAT IS IT.

"Milk Bottle" puzzle (page 71). Place your forefinger inside the loop and give the loop a quick and sharp blow sideways. You must follow through, sweeping the loop out from under the dime. The dime will then fall straight down and into the bottle.

"Soup Tureen" puzzle (page 72). There were 400 of each type of coin.

400 silver dollars = $400
400 half-dollars = $200
400 quarters   = $100
              $700

"Bug" puzzle (page 73). The answer is ten inches, and depends upon the fact that at all times the path of the pursuing bug was perpendicular to the path of the pursued bug. Because of this, the pursued bug never moved closer to, or farther away from, the pursuing bug. The pursuing bug then had only to cover the ten inches that originally separated them. As the pursued bug moved forward, the pursuing bug had to constantly adjust its forward course to the right to maintain a perpendicular course. This caused the four bugs to spiral down into the middle, where they met after travelling 10 inches each.

"Bell" puzzle (page 74). When the Durango Kid started hauling on the rope, he found himself going up in the air the same distance as the bell. When the bell was four feet off the ground, so was Durango. No matter how fast or how slowly he hauled on the rope, he was the same distance above the ground as the bell. They both arrived at the tower together, which after all was what the Reverend wanted.

"Hunter" puzzle (page 75). First, determine how many birds were present when Sir Blunder Buss let rip with his shotgun. Twice four plus twenty was a total of 28 blackbirds. He killed a seventh of them, which was four birds. These birds fell to the ground and the others flew away at the sound of the shot. So, the answer to the question of how many birds remained has to be four (the number of dead birds on the ground).

"Bishop" puzzle (page 76). The total number of bishops is fourteen. The illustration shows their placement.

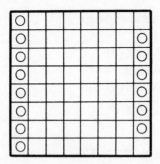

"Castle" puzzle (page 77). The girl descended first, using the cannonball as a counterweight. The king and his son then took the cannonball out of the upper basket and the son descended, with the girl acting as counterweight. They then sent the cannonball down alone and, when it reached the ground, the son got into the basket along with the cannonball. Their joint weight allowed the king to descend. The prince got out and the cannonball went down alone. The girl then went down, the cannonball ascending. The son removed the cannonball and went down alone, his sister ascending. The girl then put the cannonball in the opposite basket, and lowered herself to the ground.

"Square" puzzle (page 78).

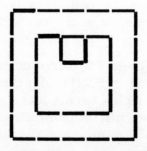

"Presidents" puzzle (page 79). President Grant took office in 1869 and President Ford left office in 1977. Within this range the only two years that read the same upside-down as they do right side up are 1881 and 1961.

"Checkers" puzzle (page 80). Black wins the day by moving 22 to 26. This makes White move 30 to 14. Black then moves 17 to 10, White moves 1 to 6, and finally Black moves 10 to 1. White cannot make a move and therefore loses.

"Web" puzzle (page 81). The following steps clearly describe the solution to the tangle:

Step 1: $20'' \times 4 = 80''$ circumference

Step 2: $\dfrac{80}{3.14} = 25.48$ diameter

Step 3: $25.48 \times 25.48 = 649.23$ (area of square)

Step 4: $\dfrac{25.48}{2} = 12.74$ (radius of circle)

Step 5: $12.74 \times 12.74 \times 3.14 = 509.65$ (area of circle)

Step 6:
$$\begin{array}{r} 649.23 \\ -\ 509.65 \\ \hline 139.58 \end{array} = \text{area of corners}$$

Step 7: $\dfrac{139.58}{4} = 34.9$ square inches (area of spider's web)

"Dictionary" puzzle (page 82). The answers are as follows: 1,D; 2,F; 3,I; 4,L; 5,P; 6,A; 7,O; 8,Q; 9,M; 10,J; 11,G; 12,B.

"Bridge" puzzle (page 83). All you have to do is to pleat the paper as shown and the puzzle is solved.

"Wineglass" puzzle (page 84). To get the coin out, blow sharply down the inside of the glass. This causes the half-dollar to turn upwards in the glass. At the same time, the dime will fly up past the half-dollar and out of the glass. Experiment with several different-size glasses to find one that works perfectly.

"Bottle and Key" puzzle (page 85). This puzzle can only be solved on a sunny day, because the string must be in line with the sun. To remove the key from the string, just take a large magnifying glass and concentrate the sun's rays through the side of the bottle onto the knot. After a few moments the knot will burn through and the key will fall to the bottom of the bottle.

"Horse" puzzle (page 86). Here's how Trevor Torts handled the case. He rode one of his own horses over to the Tralawny stable and added it to the seventeen horses of the inheritance, bringing the total to eighteen. He then gave John nine horses (half of eighteen), James six horses (one-third of eighteen), and William two horses (one-ninth of eighteen). This division disposed of the inheritance in the manner originally set forth by the Squire in his will. Having rendered a decision that satisfied all the parties involved, Trevor mounted his own horse and rode happily back home.

"Counterfeit Coin" puzzle (page 87). The contestants took one coin from hat one, two from hat two, three from hat three, and so on. When they finished, they placed their pile of fifty coins on the scale for their one weighing. If the fifty coins were all genuine, their total weight would have been 500 grams, but since one or more of the coins was counterfeit, the total weight was less. When they subtracted the weight shown by the scale from 500, the difference was the number of the hat that contained the bogus coins. For example, if the counterfeit coins were in hat number six, the scale would have showed a total weight of 494 grams, since six coins in the pile came from this hat. 494 from 500 is six, the number of the hat with the counterfeit coins.

"Ancient Coin" puzzle (page 88). They were able to share the coins evenly because there were only three people on the road—a grandfather, a father, and a son. Among them there were two fathers and two sons.

"Scholar" puzzle (page 89). It's no word at all. The answer is *a postman*.

"Automobile" puzzle (page 90). Every part of a wheel revolves around the central axis at a fixed speed when the wheel is *fixed* in place, as in the case of a waterwheel. When a wheel is in motion, like the wheels on a car, the top part of the wheel must be moving forward at a faster speed or the car wouldn't move (this is what happens when the car is caught on a patch of ice). Look at the drawing. As the wheel moves forward, from left to right, point *a*, starting at position *a1*, travels along a downward path. Note that when it reaches position *a2*, point *b* is at position *b2*. The distance that point *b* travels is a great deal less than the distance travelled by point *a*; thus, point *a* must travel at a greater rate of speed than *b* in order to cover this greater distance in the same amount of time. However, when point *a* moves from position *a2* to *a3*, point *b*'s speed increases while point *a*'s speed decreases. Thus, a point on a moving wheel travels most slowly at the bottom and fastest at the top. (Credit goes to the great English puzzler Henry Dudeny for this outstanding brainbuster.)

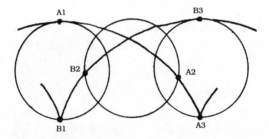

"Shield" puzzle (page 91). Start at any dot, count six dots and place a coin on the sixth dot. Remember which dot you started counting from—that's where you want to place your second coin. Start counting from a dot that allows you to come to rest on the first dot. Start the third coin so that it comes to rest on the dot you started your second coin from. Continue like this for the rest of the coins.

"Trick" puzzle (page 92). The answer to this ageless question is "time."

"Door" puzzle (page 93). Rearrange the letters to spell *one word*.

"Samurai" puzzle (page 94). Since the path ascends at a fixed rate of one in ten, when the traveller reaches the summit he has gone a distance of ten kilometres. Figure 1 shows the path as a straight line, while Figure 2 shows the same line circling up Mount Foolisama. In both cases, the distance is the same.

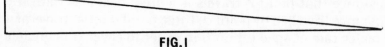

FIG. I

FIG. 2

"Eight Word" puzzle (page 95). The one thing that all eight words have in common is that each one contains three consecutive letters of the alphabet in a row.

"Train" puzzle (page 96). The answer is one mile. The trains approached each other at ten miles per hour (6 + 4 = 10). Since the horsefly started flying back and forth when the trains were a half-mile apart, they met in one-half of 10 = 1/20 of an hour. Since the horsefly travelled twenty miles an hour, he travelled one mile in 1/20 of an hour.

"Mental" puzzle (page 97). Pair the lowest and highest numbers (1 + 100 = 101; 2 + 99 = 101; 3 + 98 = 101; etc.), and you have fifty such pairs. Thus, 50 × 101 = 5050, the "mental" solution.

"Hand" puzzle (page 98). Anyone not in on the secret usually tries to slowly draw away the card, inevitably failing. The proper method is to give the corner of the card a smart snap with the second finger of the left hand. If this is done exactly right, the card will shoot away with a sort of spinning motion, the coin remaining undisturbed on your right thumb. (Our thanks to Professor Hoffmann for this clever trick.)

"Quarter" puzzle (page 99). Fold the paper exactly across the middle of the hole; then take it in both hands, and ask someone to drop the quarter into the fold. Let it rest just over the hole, its lower edge projecting below. Bend the corners of the paper slightly upwards, as indicated by the drawing. This elongates the opening, and the quarter will, after a second or two, fall through. The paper will remain uninjured. (Once again, thanks to Professor Hoffmann for this fine problem.)

"Five and Ten Cent" puzzle (page 100). The illustration shows the placement of the coins.

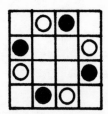

Index

s indicates solution